LANCE

HOPE
IS ALIVE

ONE ADDICT'S STORY OF HOPE

THE HOPE HANDBOOK

Published by:

2410 W. Memorial Rd.
Suite C #260
Oklahoma City, OK 73134

nxtlevel.net

ISBN: 978-0-9882096-2-6
Printed in the United States of America
Library of Congress Cataloging-in-Publication Data

For information regarding author interviews or speaking engagements, please contact the public relations department – PR@lancelang.com.

CONTENTS

FROM LANCE

Welcome! I'm so glad you've decided to join this group. Though you're going to put in a lot of work over the next eight sessions, I think you're really going to enjoy it. I believe it will help to give you the courage, confidence and accountability you need to successfully maneuver your way down this narrow path we call sobriety.

I know for many of you, achieving sobriety and getting your life back on track can seem like an insurmountable task. I know, because I've been right where you are. For a solid decade, I used and abused everything I could get my hands on, destroying every relationship in my life in the process. I lost control of my future and consumed a pile of financial debt so high I couldn't see the top. But within a few short years, through working these steps and by the grace of a loving and merciful God, I've been able to get my life back on track. And you know what? You can do the same thing! Is it easy? No.

Will it take some hard work? Absolutely. But you can do it! In fact, you've taken the hardest step by agreeing to open this book in the first place. So you're off to a good start.

Before you get rolling, I want you to know something: no matter what brought you to open this book, whether you're reading it in prison, in a treatment center, at church, in a small group, or just by yourself or with friends—you are not reading it by accident. There are no accidents in God's world. Everything has a purpose. Even your past. God knows where you've been, but more importantly He knows where you're going.

In the bible in the book of Jeremiah, there is a verse that I believe is perfectly written for folks like us. It says this"

"For I know the plans I have for you," declares the Lord, "plans to prosper you and not to harm you, plans to give you hope and a future." Jeremiah 29:11 (NIV)

God is sending you hope *right now.* You've been given a second chance, an opportunity to go and claim the future that God has prepared for you. With this newfound hope and some of the suggestions I've outlined in this book, I firmly believe you can stay sober.

I believe you can achieve more than you've ever

dreamed.

I believe your marriage can be restored.

I believe your kids can respect you again.

I believe you can get your job back.

I believe you can maintain healthy relationships.

I believe you can be all that you've ever wanted to be.

When it comes down to it, I believe that, with HOPE, anything is possible. And today my friends, Hope is Alive!

-Lance Lang,

December 2013

LEADER GUIDE

If you are the chosen one leading a group of people through this curriculum there are a few things you will need to know.

First off, don't feel pressured to have all the answers. It's okay if you don't; in fact that's probably a *good* thing. Just let the curriculum do the work and allow the individuals in your group to find out the answers for themselves through the process. The answers will mean more to them and will have a longer-lasting impact if they're able to come to their own conclusions.

Second, this curriculum was written with one very important thought in mind: that each participant would have read the corresponding chapter in the *Hope is Alive* book before attending the session. So keep this in mind when you are preparing your group for class and encourage them to come to each session having read at least a portion of the chapter.

Finally, each chapter is built in a similar structure and was done so on purpose. To help you understand why we did this, we've listed some thoughts on how to facilitate each session below:

Introduction – Set up the chairs in a circle and don't allow anyone to be in the middle or to stand out—in this program, we are all in the same position.

Start the session casually, asking everyone how their week has been leading up to tonight.

Then go around the room and ask everyone to give you a number from 1-10; 10 meaning that life is perfect and has never been better, 1 meaning life is horrible and I am not sure how I'm going to make it through the night. Allow everyone a chance to share, but keep it brief; tell them they have 1-2 minutes max.

Once everyone has given their number for the week, ask someone to read the introduction for that session aloud and then move on to the discussion questions. **This portion of the session should last about 5-10 minutes.**

Discussion Questions – As the facilitator you should ask these questions one at a time, helping the group collectively answer them by calling on someone to start. Some of the questions allow for the participant to write in their answer; when you encounter these, encourage everyone in the group to do this. For the verbal questions, as others share, encourage others to write what comes to their mind. Oftentimes what someone else says can spark a thought. Ask for at least two people to share on each question and allow for a few minutes of sharing per person. **This portion of the session should last about 15-20 minutes.**

Take Action – Action changes everything, so make sure this portion of the session is not rushed and is properly facilitated. Have all the supplies and props ready to go, along with the music already cued up. Take the lead and read through the Take Action content aloud, answering any questions and provide any motivation you feel necessary, and then let everyone go to work. This should be a time where the suggested song is played, along with any other music you deem appropriate.

Encourage the class to make this time their own, and if they need to go off into a corner let them do it. For many, taking this step of action will be challenging and sometimes even awkward, so be lead by example, jumping in and participating yourself. **This portion of the session should last**

10

about 15-20 minutes.

Closing Thought – Once everyone has wrapped up their action step for the week, bring them back into the circle. Ask for two volunteers (more if you have time) to stand up and show the class what they created and explain the meaning. This helps the class see what others are working on, therefore encouraging accountability and support. Once this is complete, if the chapter has a closing thought, then choose someone to read that out loud. **This portion of the session should last about 5 minutes.**

Prayer – This is a crucial time in the session, so please don't rush through it. These prayers are specifically written to help the class tie a bow around what they have been working on for the past week, offering all their hard work, sacrifice, and fear to God. I encourage the class to make this a special time each week. Allow someone different to close the night in prayer at the end of each session. **This portion of the session should last about 5 minutes.**

Props / Resource / Music

Session 1

- Items to have: Sharpies, Plain white bandanas (usually available at Hobby Lobby or other craft store)

- Music: Chris Tomlin – "White Flag" & "No Turning Back"
- Takeaway: Flag

Session 2:

- Items to have: Scissors
- Music: Simon & Garfunkel – "Bridge Over Troubled Water" & Not For A Moment – Vertical Church Band
- Takeaway: List of Hope Partners

Session 3:

- Items to have: Scissors
- Music: Sovereign – "Chris Tomlin & Mandisa – "Stronger"
- Takeaway: List of 5 things to incorporate into your routine

Session 4:

- Items to have: 4x6 Notecards, Colored Markers
- Music: Jason Gray - "Remind Me Who I Am" & Kristian Stanfill – "The Stand"
- Takeaway: Decorate notecard with Mandate Statement written on it

Session 5:

- Items to have: Three small stones for each participant
- Music: Elevation Worship – "Give Me Faith"
- Takeaway: the YES stones

Session 6:

- Items to have: Small Peace Sign
- Music: Matthew West - "Forgiveness", Don Henley - "Heart of the Matter"
- Takeaway: Peace Sign Emblem

Session 7:

- Items to have: A takeaway that represents people that can be held in your hand. Example a smiley face squishy ball
- Music: Michael W. Smith – "I'll Lead You Home"
- Takeaway: Smiley Face Squishy Ball

Session 8:

- Items to have: Scissors, Staplers
- Music: Switchfoot – "Dare You to Move", Big Daddy Weave – "Redeemed"
- Takeaway: Your Story of Hope!

SESSION 1
SURRENDER

Introduction:

No one likes to surrender. Especially competitive people like me. But what I have found is, the more I fight, the further away from God I fall. Surrendering is the most important part of coming to find a life of recovery. This first step is crucial. It's the building block in which the rest of the program is built. If you don't get this there's a good chance you won't get the rest of it, so be thorough and take your time.

Discussion Questions:

Have your past decisions shown surrender or a fight?

_____

Could you relate to the analogy of the frog and the boiling water? Did a crazy life become normal to you?

_____

How?

_____

Give 5 examples of how your life typified a lack of
surrender:

1. _____

2. _____

3. _____

4. _____

5. _____

What, if anything, do you see different about the following two
statements:

I can admit that I have a problem

—or—

I fully accept that I have problem

Today can you say that you have fully accepted your
addiction? If so, then who/what do you need to surrender to on
a daily basis in order to maintain your sobriety?

_____

What issues or circumstances do you need to release
your control over?

_____

_____

What are you going to do from this day forward to practice daily surrender over these areas of your life?

_____

_____

Take Action:

At the end of chapter 2 of *Hope Is Alive*, I challenged you to find a white flag, to write the phrase "I Surrender" on it, and then to place that flag over your door or in another highly visible place. Have you done this yet? If not, today is the day you do. Don't put off this step any longer.

Your group leader should have flags for everyone in the group. Distribute these and follow the instructions below:

1. Take a moment to think about your answers to the questions in this chapter.

2. With a bold, dark Sharpie, write these words on your flag: "I surrender."

3. Once everyone has done this, go around the room and allow each person in the group to share about their experience working through this chapter and what it means to them to say "I surrender" today.

4. (Optional Music) – Play song

5. Take the flag home and put it in a place where you will see it everyday. Here are some possible places: Over your door, on your rearview mirror, on your nightstand, in your bible, on a doorknob, or on a computer bag or backpack.

In a similar fashion to the way football teams slap the "play like champions today" sign or touch the school's "sacred rock" as they leave the locker room to take the field, allow this sign to be a daily reminder for you. Each time you see the flag, whether it's above your door, hanging around your rearview mirror, or on your nightstand, take the time to reach out and touch it. Even if you have to jump up and slap it. Do it! Make this a commitment.

By choosing to do this you are saying, *I am choosing to live in the solution. I resolve to say NO to my old way of doing things, my old way of thinking, my old way of acting. I know where that leads me and I don't want to go there anymore.* This is an act of daily surrender!

Closing thought:

Recently I've begun stuffing a white bandana in my back pocket. Most people think this is either a fashion statement or that I am pledging my allegiance to some gang. It's neither. What it is, is a daily visibly reminder to me that I must live a surrender life to God if I am to have any chance and staying clean and sober. Each time I see the bandana in a mirror or feel it when I sit down, I am reminded of where I have been and where God has allowed me to go since April 27th, 2011. Furthermore, when people ask me about it I am able to tell them my story. Allowing me to carry the message of recovery, hope, and surrender to another person who may need it.

As this pivotal chapter comes to an end, we're going to pray the following prayer together. And then, after this session is complete, I want you to take the time to read through this prayer alone, as many times as you feel necessary. Find a quiet place; get on your knees and prayerfully offer your surrendered soul to God.

Prayer:

God, it's clear to me as I look back on my past that I have not surrendered to your will, your timing, or your plans for my life. For that I am sorry and seek your forgiveness. With joy in my heart, I say that Today is the day I change this way of living. I am handing over all of my issues to you. Surrendering my addiction, the people who frustrate me, the circumstances I can't control, and a future that is uncertain. I am completely surrendering and acknowledging that your ways are better than mine. I choose to quit fighting, to give up, and to rest in the fact that you have a future and hope planed for me. God, grant me the serenity to accept the things I cannot change, the courage to change the things I can, and the wisdom to know the difference. But most of all God give me the strength to surrender my all to you every day. More of you, less of me. Amen!

SESSION 2
HOPE PARTNERS

Introduction:

Sobriety isn't achieved alone. We get there through the patient, loving, nurturing support and accountability of trusted mentors. "Hope Partners," as we call them—people who are going to help us achieve this goal of sobriety that for so long seemed completely unattainable. But as addicts this concept can be hard to grasp fully.

We've done things all on our own for so long that stepping up and reaching out for help can be an intimidating and humbling thought. But what you must remember is that just because you've found some early sobriety doesn't mean that life suddenly will become perfect. Life still goes on and with that will come disappointments, layoffs, tough financial decisions, legal battles, loss of loved ones, parenting struggles… and all of those *on top of* the ongoing battle to stay clean and sober.

These are just a few of the main reasons why we need a solid team around us who will keep us in line, encourage us to continue to grow, and be there to pull us up when we're down.

Hope Partners are in place for your success, the more you have, the better chance you have to stay clean.

Discussion Questions:

Do you find it hard to reach out and ask for help? Why or why not?

_____

_____

_____

Have you been legitimately successful on your own in the past?

_____

_____

When you were using, who were the people in your life? How did those people affect your life?

_____

_____

_____

Who, if anyone, did you look up to in a positive way? Did you have any mentors or partners at all?

_____

_____

Why did you look up to these people? Did they have character traits you respected? Professional skills? Quality of life? Something else?

_____

_____

Take Action:

In this chapter we have discussed why we need people in our lives, and we've identified the types of people who fit us and the different facets of Hope Partners we need. So now it's time to put some meat on these bones and make a list.

The first step is to determine the 5 people you want on your team as Hope Partners. List them below, along with which aspect(s) of their life you want to emulate and have them partner with *you* about (do you want them as a spiritual partner? as a recovery partner? as a business or industry mentor?) Once you've finished that, take some scissors and *cut your list out of this book.* Yes, you have my permission to deface this book! This is your takeaway for the week. Place it somewhere you will see it so that it will remind you of who you should be seeking out to help you along your journey.

---Optional Music---

Hope Partner List

1. _____

2. _____

3. _____

4. _____

5. _____

Now that you have your possible Hope Partners, it's time to write out exactly what you want to say in your initial approach to them. Do not try to wing this! You may be the smoothest smooth-talker since Walter White, but this is not the time nor the place to try to improvise your way into a Hope Partner relationship.

Instead, write out your introduction and learn it word for word. In case you're wondering what should go in your introduction, here are the ingredients: write out your name, a brief sentence about your addiction and your subsequent recovery, and then a couple more brief sentences about the ways you would like this person to partner with you and why. (See Chapter 3 of *Hope Is Alive* for specific ways this introduction can look.)

Once you have your introduction memorized, you can then approach the person, whether it is in person, over the phone, or through email or snail mail and see what happens!

---Optional Music---

Hope Partner Introduction:

_____

_____

_____

_____

_____

_____

_____

Closing Thought:

Look, here's the deal. This chapter and the action steps can exponentially enhance your life. Finding the right people to speak into your life changes the game in an instant. Is it hard? Of course! Is it sometimes awkward to go up to someone you barely know and ask them to help you? Heck yes! But is it worth enduring the awkwardness for the potential gain?

Absolutely! Every time. Deep down, people want to help other people. Many times they are just waiting for someone to come up and ask them. So get to asking!

Prayer:

God, I've tried for so long to do this on my own. Each time I've failed. I acknowledge that, on my own, I can't overcome the battle I'm facing. The task is too big. But I know that with you on my side and a team around me, I can do this. I can live clean and sober for the rest of my life. I can beat this addiction that has chained me down for years! So today will you help me identify and connect with the right people to help hold me accountable? I need strong people who will love me enough to make sure I follow through with what I have set out to do, so I pray You would clear a path to those people. When the time comes for me to ask them for help, I pray You would give me bold confidence to approach them. I know you love me and that I am worth this. I trust You. Thank You. Amen.

SESSION 3
GET A ROUTINE

Introduction:

I once heard in my AA home group meeting that the only thing we really needed to change to get sober is *everything*! Well, changing everything starts with pushing out the inconsistency and impulsivity that used to fill up our day-to-day living and replacing them with a solid diet of structure, consistency, and accountability. As we track through daily life, we will no doubt come across seasons of sadness, times of loss, and bouts with doubt. But if, as we are creating this newly discovered life, we incorporate times of meditation, scripture, exercise, and prayer, then we will get back the balance we lost while we were living in active addiction.

The life you will lead from here on out will be measurably different, and in a great way! But setting yourself up for a successful and sustained sobriety takes creating a routine that stimulates you and motivates you to keep going, to keep pushing forward. The more you stay focused and plugged in to your routine, the stronger you will get.

We will never get to a point where we are strong enough to abandon routine, but as our strength grows, we will begin to receive the fruits of this labor as we pass along to others what we have learned along our journey. And *that* is the greatest gift of all!

Discussion Questions:

When you look back on your time drinking, using, or acting out, did you ever maintain a solid routine?

_____

_____

In the past, can you see where you were more productive and stable when your life was more structured?

_____

_____

What was your physical fitness like when you were using?

_____

_____

What does it feel like to start your day on your knees in prayer?

_____

_____

_____

Take Action:

I have expanded on my routine since I finished writing *Hope Is Alive*. You will probably also come to find that, as you make progress through your recovery, your routine will adjust and change. That's okay; that's natural. But for today, right now, you need to focus on nailing down *at least* five things you are going to do every day to ensure you stay in the proper state of mind, soul, and sobriety.

Fortunately, you don't have to think of those things off the top of your head! Here is a long list of recovery-based activities I've collected over the past few years. Implementing five of these types of actions into your daily life will help you keep your routine focused on recovery, so read through this list and circle five (or more) things you want to incorporate into your daily routine:

28

- Start your day on your knees in prayer
- Read page 417 of the Big Book of Alcoholics Anonymous.
- Find a daily devotional to read each morning
- Read a chapter from Proverbs each day
- Maintain a daily Bible-reading plan
- Meditate for five minutes each day
- Recite scripture
- Get up at the same time every day
- Call other people in recovery every day
- Go for a daily run or walk
- Lift weights
- Take a yoga class
- Read a recovery blog
- Make your bed every morning
- Be still the first 30 minutes of each day
- Write out a gratitude list every day at lunchtime
- Listen to a special song
- Take a daily "good, bad, and ugly" inventory of what you've done

During this session, your mind has probably been on overdrive as you contemplate *how* you are going to incorporate five new things into your day, which is probably already crazy-busy.

Well, one tip to help you get started is this: make appointments with yourself. Set up a consistent time every day for you to check off some of the activities you have chosen to incorporate into your daily routine. For example: if you chose to take a daily inventory, then set an alarm on your phone to ring at 2:00 each afternoon. When the alarm goes off, take a moment to think about what you've done throughout that day. Have you encouraged someone else? Have you gotten angry? Have you stayed in your routine? Have you hurt someone? Have you hurt yourself?

The more we begin to build on our routine and life begins to get better it can become very common to lose touch with our routine, so scheduling a time every day to check ourselves helps us stay grounded, humbled, and sober.

As people in recovery, we know that structure and consistency are key components to our overall success. Today, take a moment to review the tips and suggestions I just laid out and when you're finished, write down those five things you circled onto the list below:

1. _____

2. _____

3. _____

4. _____

5. _____

Now, use scissors to cut out this section of your workbook. This list of daily activities will be your takeaways from this chapter; over the next week and through the rest of the sessions, keep this piece of paper with you at all times. It will be a physical reminder to solidify these action steps and incorporate them into your daily life.

Prayer:

God, thank you that today I don't have to live in chaos. I am so thankful that You have helped me to find a life that is full of peace, joy, and stability. Today I pray You will help me to overcome my impulsive tendencies and stay focused on the routine I am developing through this program. I need more structure to stay sober. I need a plan. But most importantly I need You to help me live it out every day. Today I put my schedule, my outline, and my day-to-day life in Your hands. Use them. Guide me where You want me to be. Amen.

SESSION 4
MAKE A MANDATE

Introduction:

Every organization in existence has a mandate statement. They may call it something different, like a mission or vision statement, or they may wrap it up in a box and call it their core values, but no matter how they label it, they have something they live by, something that directs them and guides them toward their end goal.

So if millions of companies and individuals have statements driving them each and every day, then it makes sense that those of us trying to change our lives completely could follow their lead. As I wrote in the chapter of *Hope Is Alive* that you read in preparation for this session, our mandate statement is yet another reinforcing element that we must mix into the foundation we are pouring. This critical piece to puzzle should represent the core of who you are.

For me, I knew the statement "I will not use no matter what" was perfect the moment I heard it. Why? Because I knew that I would have times of ultimate temptation. Moments in which drugs and alcohol would be readily available and come with little immediate consequence. So I needed a statement that would slap me across the face when I faced those times, a barrier that wouldn't move. *No matter what!*

Maybe that's exactly what you need. Maybe the perfect statement for you is the kind that clarifies what you can *not* do.

Or maybe that doesn't fit your personality or program— that's okay as well. Maybe instead, you need a mandate that explores who you are at your deepest core.

Or maybe you need a motivational mandate, something that focuses on positivity to help you continue moving forward in your recovery—that's okay, too.

There's no right or wrong way to frame your mandate statement. As I often say, your recovery is yours! So make this personal to *you*. As you answer the following discussion questions, allow God to help you craft a mandate that perfectly fits you.

Discussion Questions:

How you are best motivated? Fear? Inspiration? Encouragement? Challenge?

_____

_____

_____

Has a mandate statement already stuck out to you? If so, what is it? Why do you relate to this statement?

_____

_____

_____

What do you think needs to go into _your_ mandate statement?

_____

_____

_____

How effective do you think a mandate statement would/ could be for you?

_____

_____

_____

_____

Take Action:

Write down 5 words that call you to action:

1. _____

2. _____

3. _____

4. _____

5. _____

Now write down 5 words that motivate you:

1. _____

2. _____

3. _____

4. _____

5. _____

Write down 5 words that remind you of where you've

been:

1. _____

2. _____

3. _____

4. _____

5. _____

And now write down 5 words that describe where you want to go:

1. _____
2. _____
3. _____
4. _____
5. _____

Now look back through these lists. What words really jump off the page?

_____

_____

Which ones best describe who you really are? What do you want to do? What you can't do?

_____

_____

Using these words and the ideas/thoughts you got from your discussion time, write your mandate statement here:
---Optional Music---

_____

_____

_____

_____

As a takeaway this week, I want you to transfer your mandate from this page to a note card that your group leader will provide you. As the music plays, write your mandate on this note card. Decorate it if you'd like. Make it special and unique to you. Keep this with you during the upcoming week and pull it out anytime you need to remind yourself of who you are really are.

---Optional Music---

Closing Thought:

If you need some ideas or inspiration for your statement, here are some examples of mandate statements I have collected as I have traveled across the country teaching this curriculum:

- Today I choose to live clean, because I am worth it!
- Never again will I let the lies of the enemy shape who I really am.
- It's not worth it, no matter what happens I will NOT drink!
- One day at a time, I will maintain the strength, confidence, and passion I need to stay clean.
- I can do this! God has given me everything I will

ever need to beat this today!

- I know I am creative, compassionate, and loving. When I use, I lose all of these great gifts.

- God is not in love with a future version of me, He loves me as I am and will never leave my side.

- I have forgiven who I need to forgive; now I live like I am supposed to live!

- I am a mighty warrior ready to overcome, whatever comes my way!

- When I am weak, you are strong. When I am strong, you are stronger!

Prayer:

God, I pray You will embolden me to live out this mandate on my life. Help me to embrace it and to use it when I need it. I know there are times when I try to get outside of your plan for my life so I pray this statement will help act as a rudder that will steer me back in line with you. I commit this mandate to You, praying that You will bless it mightily. Your word says I can do all things through Your Son who provides me strength. So I ask that You please give me the strength I need to live out my mandate today. In your name I pray, Amen.

SESSION 5

JUST SAY 'YES'!

Introduction:

Out of all the chapters in the book, this one has the ability to exponentially change your life. How? Let me give you just one example.

In November of 2012, one of my Hope Partners told me that my story needed to be on paper and challenged me to write a book. I balked at first, telling him that, in addition to me not being a writer, my story's not that special or unique. But my Hope Partner wouldn't quit encouraging me, so, soon after that day, I decided that I needed to say YES. I told myself, *Yes, I will try to write a book.*

Six months later, that book was out and my life was completely changed.

This simple, three-letter response changed everything about me. God used my obedience and willingness to touch the lives of thousands of people. *You are one them.* But even more than the impact *Hope Is Alive* has made on people, it's made an even bigger impact on me. How? Because, by saying YES to putting my life in print for the whole world to see, God did something inside of me I will never forget. He fortified my dependence on Him and put me in a position where the only direction I could look was up.

Nothing can change a life quite like blind obedience can. It's the birthplace of faith. When we put ourselves out there, taking a risk to help another or calling out of the blue to check on someone, God uses that willingness to bolster our soul and give us momentum to successfully tackle another day.

Saying YES is the attitude of someone completely surrendered to a new way of living.

Saying YES shows our community that we are truly different.

I believe that when we appear before God in glory, submitted to the Creator, He will look at us and as ask us these questions:

Were you willing?
Were you obedient?
Did you say YES?

Discussion Questions:

What are five things you used to say NO to?

1. _____

2. _____

3. _____

4. _____

5. _____

Do you say NO to these requests or petitions on a seasonal basis?

_____

What was your main motivation for saying NO?

_____

What have you learned about the power of saying YES?

_____

Do you believe there are areas of your life that could be improved if you started saying YES?

_____

What have you said YES too recently that has shown you how powerful this tool can be?

_____

_____

_____

Take Action:

Read pages 109-112 of *Hope Is Alive*. Consider the analogy of the wall used in that passage, reflect on it, and then think about this: what are some of the bricks in *your* wall? Write them down in the space below:

_____

_____

_____

_____

Today I want challenge you to think about three things that you could say YES to over the course of the next Session. Three things that will help you break through this wall. Think through what you're going to encounter in the upcoming session (which is about keeping peace in your life), and think about the decisions you'll have to make. And now that you've thought it through, write three healthy, beneficial things you'll say YES to next session:

---Optional Music---

_____

_____

_____

_____

Next session, during the sharing time, I want you to tell the group about your experience saying YES to these items. What did it feel like to say YES to something you've said NO to for so long? What came of the experience? Was it positive? Negative? Neutral? What is like to say YES when, for so long, you said NO?

Closing Thought:

A YES breaks down the anxiety that a NO has been building up inside of you for so long. When you say YES to something new or something challenges you, you take all the power out of the unknown and grab your destiny with both hands. As a physical reminder of the power of saying YES you group leader is going to give you three small stones. On each of these stones I want you to write the word YES. Throughout this upcoming week, carry these three stones in your pocket, and each time you are confronted with the decision to say YES to a new, *positive* opportunity, I want you to reach into your pocket, grab the stone, hand it to the person you are speaking with, and say YES!

Remember, the outcome doesn't matter—that's God's territory. All you are responsible for is being obedient to saying

44

YES to what He puts in front of you. Say YES today!

Prayer:

God, for so long I have been afraid to step out in faith and try something new. My addiction has locked me up in prison without a key. But today I am ready to break out and break free of these chains that have held me back for so long. Will You please give me the courage and the confidence to take these steps of faith and obedience. I rely on Your strength and assurance. I know that, as I continue to turn my will over to Yours through these actions, You will strengthen my dependence on You and teach me new things. I pray my mind and heart will be open to seeing and hearing all that You teach me through saying YES to Your will, not mine. I trust You in every YES. Amen.

SESSION 6
KEEP THE PEACE

Introduction:

Peace can be fragile. It must be maintained and guarded with care, because the way life unfolds is that eventually, somewhere along the line, *something* will happen to you that threatens your peace. Disappointments are just part of the experience of being human, so *now's* the time to get a game plan for the way you will handle those disappointments, instead of letting them catch you by surprise and possibly drive you into relapse.

Let me tell you something: life can be really difficult. Even in sobriety. I know from experience. I've had more depressing and trying times during my sobriety than I ever did while I was out getting high. Life has thrown me some major curve balls the last few years, from unexpected career news to troubled relationships to parenting problems. And in every instance, they presented the very real possibility of tripping my trigger a time or two.

This is the very reason why I've come to believe that taking steps to identify the risk in our lives and then putting plans of prevention in place are critically important pieces of the puzzle of sobriety. The truth is, guilt, shame, and resentments are sparked during the moments of pain, disappointment, and conflict. If we don't learn to stay balanced and get a plan in place to maintain the peace in our lives during these seasons, then we are fighting an uphill battle.

Peace is never permanent. You must have a plan to keep it.

Discussion Questions:

What are some ways you have responded to disappointment in the past? Have you changed those? How?

_____

How did you respond to the mansion metaphor in this chapter? Did you see yourself in it? Could you relate? Why or why not?

_____

_____

Does the prospect of "keeping the peace" or "guarding your heart" feel easy for you? Difficult? Somewhere in between?

_____

_____

Take Action:

Did you do the challenge in the book? If not, let's reexamine it here.

For starters, you need to think of three people who are *currently in your life* who might be some sort of trigger for you, who could possibly threaten to derail your peace, for whatever reason. Write their names in the spaces below:

---Optional Music---

_____

_____

_____

Got them? Good.

Now, think of three possible situations you have coming up in the next year when you might have your peace threatened. This could be anything from the usual stuff (family gatherings and holidays) to stuff that's more specific to you (court dates or the looming death of a loved one). You may even want to get out a calendar for reference or to help you think this one through deeply. Once you have them, write those three situations down on the lines below:

---Optional Music---

_____

_____

_____

And this is where your Hope Partners come into the picture. Because now that you've identified the people and situations where you might find your peace threatened, you can talk about those things with your Hope Partners. Refer to pages 129-130 of *Hope Is Alive* to find out how all those conversations should go. It might be hard, but it's worth it.

Throughout this session we have worked to identify the hurdles that keep us from living with peace in our hearts. Although identification and preparation are keys to overcoming triggers in the moment, I believe forgiveness of those people and circumstances is just as crucial. When it comes to keeping peace in your life and moving beyond the pains of the past, the heart of the matter is always forgiveness. As you listen to this song, I challenge you to submit to God all of those people, places, and things that have caused you to trip in the past. As you submit them to God, ask that he will create in you a gracious and reconciliatory spirit.

The takeaway in this session is the peace sign. It's a universal symbol of peace, but today I challenge you to connect to this symbol the character and circumstances in your life that you are choosing to forgive. Hold this symbol with you during the week, and each time you see it or touch it, take a moment to offer up a prayer of forgiveness to the people and circumstance in your life that have caused you to lose your peace. As you do this, God will build in you the strength to move past these hurts and towards a life of freedom and hope.

Prayer:

God, as I've worked through this chapter and the past session, several disturbing thoughts have come back into my mind. I can now see how easily my peace can be disrupted and my emotions swayed. So today I bring all of that to You. All the people, the circumstances, the past emotions, the hurt, the pain, the guilt, and the shame... I bring all these things to Your feet and give them to You. I pray You will walk with me through

life from here on out. Guarding my back, holding my hand,
and clearing the path in front. And when a situation arises that
jeopardizes my peace, God, I pray You would give me a way
out like You promised You would. Help me to see it clearly, and
with faith take the step towards You. Amen.

SESSION 7
GIVE IT AWAY

Introduction:

If you've gotten to this point in your sobriety, then you most likely know one thing very, very well: you are only here because other people have helped you get here. Yes, you've done some heavy lifting yourself, but others have encouraged you, have sat with you in the midst of your despair, have worked with you, have made sacrifices in their own lives so that you could get yours back on track.

And now the time has come for you to give back.

It doesn't have to be flashy and it doesn't have to be out in the open, but you do need to learn to give away the blessings you've been given. Why? Because it ultimately strengthens you and helps you keep a firm footing on the road to recovery.

So let's talk about giving back, what that looks like, and what it will take.

Discussion Questions:

How does it feel to know other people have sacrificed for you? Do you have trouble accepting their help or believing you're worth it? Why or why not?

_____

_____

How do you feel about giving back? Do you feel qualified or equipped to help others? Why or why not?

_____

_____

What are some of your natural gifts and talents that you might be able to give away to others?

_____

_____

Name one aspect of your personal story that you think could benefit someone else. How?

_____

_____

Take Action:

I am sure many of you have already begun thinking about ways you could start giving back. It's a pretty cool thought, huh? To imagine you have something that someone else needs is an empowering feeling.

Take some time as you listen to this song to consider the people who have given so much for you to be where you are, the people who have helped you in some way as you've earned your sobriety, the men and women who have lead you back home to a life of freedom, love and acceptance. Write down their names below.

_____

_____

_____

_____

_____

_____

_____

_____

_____

Now, I want you to imagine that a year from now, someone else, someone like you, is working through this very program. Imagine they get to this chapter and, when thinking about the people who helped them, they write *your* name on one of those lines.

That's the type of impact you could have on someone. On dozens, or even hundreds of people.

What are you going to do?

Who are you going to impact?

Your group leader should have a takeaway for you this week that will represent the hundreds of people that you will now have the opportunity to impact. As each of you holds this takeaway, I want you to imagine who it may represent. Does it represent your brother who is struggling still? Does is represent your mother that you can now support and love fully and compassionately? Does it represent the children in your life now or in the future? Those kids that you can now take care of, provide for and protect? Take a moment and listen to this next song as you think about all that you want to give back to this world. The impact you want to make on your family, your friend and your community. Realize that it's all within your reach now that you clean and sober.

You deserve this new life….and so do they!

---Optional Music---

Finding people to help is something that will probably happen on the spur of the moment—after all, you can't help people until they get to a place where they are ready to accept your help. But you *can* determine in advance some of the ways you can help someone, what you might have to give back. It could be anything from your time to your wisdom to your story to some of your personal resources. Take a moment to prayerfully consider the skills or traits you might have to offer someone in need and write them here.

_____

_____

_____

_____

_____

_____

_____

_____

_____

_____

_____

And now all you need to do is keep your eyes open and your heart ready to respond to a need you see. Are you willing?

Prayer:

God, I am blown away at how much You love me, so much that You would give me a second chance to change my life. This free gift of sobriety and hope has changed everything about me. But I know I have not done this on my own. I know on my own I am a mess. But thanks to You, I have new HOPE today. You have sent people across my path who have helped me get to where I am now, and I'm so thankful for those people. I pray you'll bless them for the sacrifices they've made on my behalf. I also pray that you'll help me find ways to bless others who are in need of Your help. Show me opportunities to provide practical assistance to people so that I can give back what You've so freely given to me. Thank You, Jesus. Amen.

SESSION 8
~~MY~~ YOUR STORY

Introduction:

You made it! Congratulations! I know working through these sessions has not been easy, so a big high-five to you for working hard, getting this stuff into your heart, and finishing strong.

I opened *Hope Is Alive* by telling you about my story. About my childhood, how I was raised and some of the trials I faced during early adulthood. This part of my journey was not easy to tell, but what I have found is that the more I share about my past, the more others are able to share about theirs. As I open up, people around me are given the freedom to open up as well, and healing can begin to take place.

We all have stories to tell, and a big part of your recovery going forward will be telling people all about yours, which is what this bonus session is all about. So what does your story consist of? Well, it's pretty simple: all you need to do is talk about where you were, what happened, and where you are now.

As you begin to carry the message and live out your program, you will have opportunities to tell others your story. This is very important for you and for those that are listening. As you tell your story it will bolster your internal sobriety. Your fortitude, your momentum, and your passion for life will grow, while those who hear your story will experience where you have been and where you are today, quickly discovering that they are not alone. They will find strength and encouragement from hearing what's happened to you.

So you need to know your story. It's powerful. It's life-changing! No matter where you have been, how much time you have or how many times you have attempted sobriety before, your story is special and unique. You have come alive, and if your past was anything like mine, that's a miracle in and of itself. You have been given an amazing second chance. This story of yours could change the world!

Take Action:

In this last session, we are going to spend the majority

of our time writing our stories. We've left you several pages to fill up with all the crazy stories, memories, and certainly the HOPE that you have found.

This story is your final takeaway from the class. Take some scissors if you want and cut it out and staple it up. This is your first book. Your story of HOPE. I challenged you to share with someone, so get out and start telling people about what you have gone through and how God has helped you get to the other side. Remember, this journey of sobriety is best traveled with partners. And the more you share, the more partners you will find.

Your story means something. Your story will give someone hope. And HOPE is alive.

---Optional Music---

_____

_____

_____

_____

_____

_____

_____

_____